In the Treehouse

Ladybird

One day, the Munch Bunch were sitting rather sadly in Andy Apricot's little house. It was raining so hard they couldn't go to Pip Park and play. There was nothing to do.

The Bunch didn't know what colour to choose. They all had their own favourites.

Then Sally had an idea. "Why don't we paint the walls *all* the colours?" she said.

"Surprise!" said Rozzy Raspberry. "Do you like the colour? It took me ages to paint it!"

The Bunch were speechless for a moment.

Then Andy piped up, "It's very dark. I think we should repaint the walls orange."

"No, yellow's a better colour," said Barney.

The next morning, the Bunch were in for a big surprise. When they climbed their new ladder to their new Treehouse they found...

it was bright purple!

"We should paint our Treehouse a pretty colour!" suggested Sally.

But the Bunch were very tired. They decided to finish the painting after they'd had a good night's sleep.

When the Bunch returned to Pip Park, Ollie had arrived with his plans, so Barney got to work.

He hammered and sawed and chiselled and chopped, and soon the last piece of the roof was put in place.

to the big tree that stood in a corner.
It was perfect—for a Treehouse.

Not too muddy, too hilly or too
far away.

Andy organised everyone, and the
Bunch collected the wood from
Barney's workshop using his
racing cart.

So the Bunch went home to change into their shoes and then they continued their search.

They searched every nook and every cranny. Suddenly Andy had an idea. He took the Bunch to Pip Park, and pointed up and up...

The Bunch searched all over Munch Town, but nowhere seemed quite right. Wherever they looked, it was either too muddy, too hilly, or too far away.

But luckily the rain had begun to stop and the sky was brightening up.

Meanwhile, the rest of the Bunch put on their wellington boots and rushed out into the rain to search for a place to put the Treehouse. They hoped they wouldn't get too wet!

The Bunch got to work. Ollie sat down with a big piece of paper and a pen and a ruler to draw the plans.

"Ollie can design it," said Rozzy.

"And Barney can build it," added Bertie.

"Then we can all decorate it," said Andy.

Andy suddenly jumped up.

"What we need, is a Treehouse!" he said. "Then we can play whatever the weather is like!"

"Hooray!" said the others. "What a great idea!"

Now, when it rains, it doesn't matter. The Bunch can play in their Treehouse – and they all agree it was a really good idea!

"Yes, we could paint them stripy!" suggested Bertie.

And so they did. Soon, the Treehouse was finished. It was very smart.

Once you've collected all the puzzle pieces you can make
this super Munch Bunch picture!